HAP

by Mandy Peterson

illustrations by Michael Chesworth

Harcourt Brace & Company

Orlando Atlanta Austin Boston San Francisco Chicago Dallas New York Toronto London

Hap! Hap!

I can not find Hap.

Rap. Rap.

Tap. Tap.

I see Hap in my cap!

Come down, Hap!

Come and nap.